Stepping Stones

A Beka Book® Reading Program

by
Laurel Hicks *and*
Marion Hedquist

illustrated by
Brian Jekel and Walter Kerr

PENS

To the Teacher

Stepping Stones is the third reader in the *A Beka Book* first grade reading program. It reviews special sounds introduced in Charts 6 and 7 and introduces words with new special sounds contained in Charts 8 and 9. Students should begin *Stepping Stones* after they have completed *Tiptoes*. As they read *Stepping Stones,* they should continue reading corresponding pages in *A Handbook for Reading.*

Students will enjoy these stories about children and animals while gaining fluency in reading.

The following Christian virtues and character traits are incorporated in the stories: cheerfulness, cleanliness, industry, kindness, obedience, thankfulness, and thoughtfulness.

Fourth Edition

Contents

Chart 8
Stories and Poems

Chart 9
Stories and Poems

thr
in three
3

thrill	throne	thrift	throb
three	thrash	thrust	thrive

One, Two, Three

Three green fish
Swam in the sea.
Dip and dive, dip and dive,
Please play with me!

Three fast dogs
Ran by the tree.
Zip and zap, zig and zag,
Please play with me!

Jan and Deb
Came one day for tea,
Hop and skip, run and jump,
Just we three!

ar
in stars

The stars shine
in the dark.

I like to play in the park.

Can you do a hard
job well?

Mark's dad is smart.

art	farm	bark	barn/yard
Clark	harm	spark	street/car

Words to Watch For

hard   park   drive/way

yard   in/side

Contraction: **don't = do not***

Advanced words: **was, why***

Start the Car

"I tried three times and I can't start my car," Mom said to Dad one day.

"Let me try," Dad said. He went to the driveway.

"I drove to the vet and it was fine," Mom said.

Dad said, "Hm."

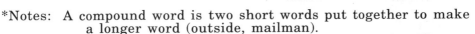

*Notes: A compound word is two short words put together to make a longer word (outside, mailman).

A contraction is a quick way of saying two words. The apostrophe shows that a letter or letters have been left out.

Advanced words contain special sounds that have not yet been taught.

"It is not a hard car to start," Mom said. "Why can't it go?"

Dad said, "Hm."

"I don't park it in the yard. I park it inside. Why can't it go?"

Dad said, "Hm." Then he said, "I see why it can't go. This car is like I am. It likes to eat. It just needs gas."

Mom said, "Hm."

Think and answer ■■■■■■■■
Why did Mom say, "Hm"?

ch
in church

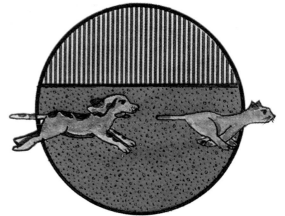

We go to church each
Sunday.

Don't chase my cat,
Spot!

Mom will chat with
Miss Smith.

The rat likes to eat
cheese.

chain	chose	branch	chest
charm	choke	chill	chart

or

in morning

born	pork	short	porch
morn	cork	sport	forth

Trust in the Lord.

back and forth

sniff and snort

big and short

beans and corn

Words to Watch For
Sight words: **your, oh***
Advanced words: **was, find, took, what**

Do You See My Corn?

The pig sat up in his pen. It was time to eat.

"I do not see my corn," he said to the sheep. "It is time for my corn. Do you see it?"

The sheep came to the pen. "No, I do not see your corn," he said.

*Note: Sight words are words that cannot be sounded out using the basic rules of phonics.

He laid his neck on the gate. "But I do see a mess in that pen. It must be time to clean it. You cannot eat lunch in such a mess."

The pig gave a snort.

"Clean this fine pen? Pigs do not clean pens!" He went back and forth, but he still did not see his corn.

The horse came by the pen. His black mane shone in the sun.

Think and answer ■ ■ ■ ■ ■ ■
Why do you think the pig is having such a hard time finding his corn?

"Do you see my corn?" the pig said.

The horse held his nose and said, "Pig, you will not find the corn in that mess. Ugh! That mud must be up to your chin. It is time to clean that pen!"

The horse took a quick step back. "I cannot chat with my feet in the mud," he said. He ran to the road.

The pig just gave a snort and tried to find his corn.

Just then the chick/en spoke up. "I can see the corn," she said. "It got hid/den in the mud."

Then she spoke to the chicks. "You must not let your home be a mess like that."

The chicks said, "Cheep."
That means, "Oh, no—not
us."

The pig got his lost corn.
It was caked with mud.

"I cannot eat this corn,"
he said. "I will choke on it."
He was one sad pig. "It is
time to clean my pen," he
said. And that is what he
did.

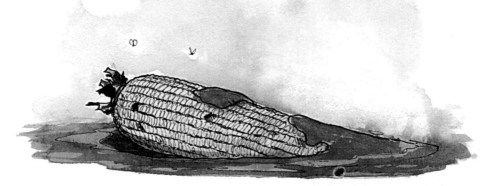

Think and answer ■ ■ ■ ■ ■ ■ ■
Do you think the pig learned a lesson?
What can *you* learn from the story?

ou
in out

out	found
our	pound
flour	shout

ow
in owl

how	brown
cow	town
down	clown

··

in and out

··

up and down

··

smile and frown

··

blue and brown

··

Let the cat
out, Tim.

"Ow! The duck bit me!"

"Bow-wow!" said the dog.

trout	sound	growl
snout	pound	scowl

mouth   round   frown

Advanced word: **was**

Jan's Clown

Jan's clown had a big red mouth. But he did not smile.

His mouth was in a frown. His nose was big and round.

Jan found a jar of grape jam and gave it to him. Still he did not smile.

"Please, Clown, try to be glad," Jan said.

"I will let you have this crown. I will let you ride my bike."

But still the clown did not smile. He just kept his mouth in a frown.

Jan is glad that she can smile. Can you?

Think and answer ▪▪▪▪▪▪▪▪
Who was cheerful, Jan or the clown?

ow
in bowl

snow   slow

blow   row

grow   show

Snow

Will it snow?

I hope so!

Then we can make a
snow/man. Dave will show
us how, and we can slide
down the hill on our sled!

I do hope it will snow!

Read and Think

Circle the special sounds.
Then read these words as fast as you can.

chant	torn	arm
cheat	thorn	ark
chart	shorn	shark
chest	storm	clark

scout	wow	row
spout	plow	blown
shout	brown	crow
trout	crown	flown

Read and Think

Write a word to rhyme with the words in each list.

1. crunch
   punch
   munch

2. thorn
   shorn
   morn

3. dark
   spark
   Mark

Words to Watch For
maybe
Sight word: **have**
Advanced words: **what, comes**
Contraction: **isn't = is not**

The Snow Day

Tim and Sport ran into the house. Tim was tired, but he gave Mom a big grin.

"What fun!" he said. "Did you see my snowman, Mom? Isn't he big?"

"Yes, he is!" Mom said. "You and Sport have had quite a day." Sport went to lie by the fire.

"It is so much fun to play in the snow," Tim said.

"Next time I will make a snow fort. Maybe I can hide in the fort and throw snow at Dad as he comes home."

Now Mom had a grin. "If you do that, I hope you can run fast!" she said.

Think and answer ∎∎∎∎∎∎∎∎

Why do you think Mom told Tim that she hoped he could run fast?

er
in verse

ur
in nurse

Mark the correct word.

This plant is a ___.
fern   turn
○   ○

Can you say this ___?
burn   verse
○   ○

The Lord is my Shepherd

One day she may
be a ___.
nurse   purse
○   ○

curl   nerve   turn   spurt   serve

ir

in bird

We will not hurt
the ___.

shirt   bird
O   O

God made the ___ tree.

fir   sir
O   O

Curt lets Ann go ___.

first   firm
O   O

skirt   birth   third   thirst   curve

The Bird Nest

One day Chad found a bird nest in the fir tree.

He ran to tell Barb. "Come quick, Barb," he said. "See what I have found."

"Oh, look!" said Barb. "I see birds in the nest. Let me count them."

"You wait your turn," said Chad. "I found these birds, and I want to count them first."

"I'm here now," said Barb. "You just wait your turn."

Chad gave Barb a push. Barb fell down to the ground.

Think and answer ▪ ▪ ▪ ▪ ▪ ▪ ▪
Are Chad and Barb being kind to each other?

Chad felt bad.

"Barb, are you hurt?" he said. "I did not mean to hurt you. Let me help you up. We will not have fun if we act like this."

"I'm not hurt. I will be fine," said Barb.

"You may look first, Barb," said Chad.

"We can both count the birds," said Barb. "Two can count as well as one."

And Barb and Chad both said, "One, two, three!"

Think and answer ■ ■ ■ ■ ■ ■ ■
What important lesson did Chad and Barb learn about being friends?

Read and Think

Read these words as fast as you can.

burn	nerve	twirl	grow
spurn	serve	swirl	snow

• •

Draw lines to match the rhyming words.

cow	loud	flown	grown
proud	how	crown	frown

• •

How smoothly can you read the sentences?

1. Tom hurt his arm on the tree branch.
2. Kim got a red skirt at the store.

The Best Day

"R-r-r," said the clock by Jane's bed.

"Get up, Jane, get up!" said Sue.

"I don't want to get up yet," Jane said. "I want to go back to sleep."

"Not today," said Sue. "This is the best day of the week."

"The best day of the week?" Jane said. "Is it the day we go down town?"

"No," said Sue. "It's not the day we go down town."

"Then is it the day we have hot dogs at lunch?"

Think and answer ....
What day do *you* think it is?

"No," said Sue. "It's not hot dog day."

"Well, I give up, then," Jane cried. "What day is it, Sue?"

"It's Sunday," said Sue. "It's the day we go to church."

"Sunday!" Jane cried. "That's the best day of the week."

Jane got up fast. She put on her red skirt and blouse. Sue put on her blue skirt and blouse. And they both ran down to eat.

Then Sue and Jane and Mom and Dad got into the car to go to church.

"I like Sunday," said Jane.
"It's the best day of the
week."

Think and answer ■■■■■■■
Why is Sunday the best day?

oi
in coin

oy
in boy

oil	joy	point	Troy
coy	join	champ	gown
burst	glow	sprout	

This coin is a dime.

Seeds grow well in moist soil.

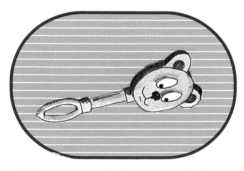

The toy fell out of the crib.

Roy is a fine boy.

Words to Watch For

ground	mouse	twirl
boy	Troy	point

Advanced words: **thank, push**

Stop That Top!

One day I met a fine boy.
He said his name was Troy.

"I like you," I said to Troy.
"You may play with my top."

"Thank you," said Troy.
You see, he was a fine boy.

Troy gave the top a twirl.
It made a loud noise and
went out the door.

"Stop that top!"
said Troy.

Think and answer ∎∎∎∎∎∎∎
How do we know that Troy was a fine boy?

The top did not stop. It kept its point to the ground. It went on, round and round.

A mouse came to see what the noise was.

"Stop that top!" said Troy.

The mouse did not stop the top. She just ran back to her house.

The top went down the path. A bird came to see what the noise was.

"Stop that top!" said Troy.

"Such a lot of noise!" the bird said, but she did not stop the top. She just went back home with a hop.

"We must stop that top," said Troy. "Help me, please," he said to me.

I tried to help. I ran up to the top and tried to pick it up. It hit my arm. "Ouch," I said, but the top went on down the path to the farm.

"Stop, Top!" Troy and I cried.

Still the top did not stop.

Just then a pig
came down the path.

"Stop that top,
Pig!" said Troy.

The pig gave the top a
hard push with his nose.

The top fell on its side
and came to a stop.

The pig sat down on the
path. He held the top.

"Do you see what I see?"
said Troy. "The pig likes the
top."

"I will let him have it," I
said. "We had fun with the
top. Now the pig can have a
turn."

And Troy and I went down
the path to my house.

Think and answer ■ ■ ■ ■ ■ ■ ■
Why did the boys give the top to the pig?

oo
in book

cook	stood	good	south
took	wood	hood	perk

Will the brook rise?

This is the best book.

Mother shook the rug out.

Note: *oo* can say ŏŏ (book) or ōō (tooth). Common words that are exceptions are flood, blood, door, floor.

oo

in tooth

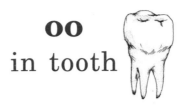

goose	boot	spoon	squirm
loose	hoot	moo	foil

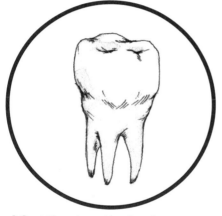

Matt's tooth is loose.

I like my red boots.

This good food is a gift from God.

What Boys Like

"Come on, Todd," said Dad. "Let's go see the jets take off."

"Do you mean it?" said Todd. "I'll be with you as soon as I give Spot his food."

Todd ran out to the dog-house and fed his pet. Then he met Dad in the driveway.

"Hop in," said Dad. "I'll need to get gas first."

"Fill it up, please," he said to the man.

Soon Dad and Todd were on the way.

"I can see them!" cried Todd. "Look at those planes out there!"

Think and answer ▪▪▪▪▪▪▪▪
Where do you think Todd's dad got gas?

"Let's stop here and get out," said Dad. "Then you can get a good look at them."

"Wow! Look at that big one!" Todd cried. "It looks like a big bird."

Zoom! The big jet took off with a loud noise.

"No bird can fly that fast," said Todd.

"Come on, Todd," Dad said. "It's time to go home. Next week we can go to the zoo if you do a good job on your room."

"Thank you, Dad," said Todd. "You know just what boys like to do."

Think and answer ■ ■ ■ ■ ■ ■ ■ ■

Do you think Todd will try to do a good job on his room? Why?

Should he always keep his room neat?

Read and Think

  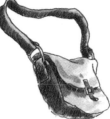

Read these words as fast as you can.

point   joy   chop   foot   tool

berth   purse   throw   pouch   cart

* * *

Mark the correct word.

1. Cows say _____.

   "cluck"   "moo"   "quack"
     O   O   O

2. A goose is a big _____.

   bird   house   boy
    O   O   O

3. A sheep gives us _____.

   couch   roost   wool
    O   O   O

wor
in worms

igh
in night

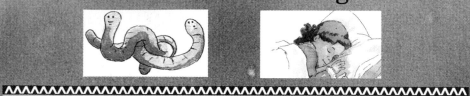

| work | worth | worms | world |

Good Night

Good night,
Sleep tight.
Wake up bright
In the morning light,
To do what's right
With all your might.

| high | tight | sight | boy |
| sigh | fright | might | chimes |

Advanced word: **all**

Words to Watch For

cork   work   branch   horn

north   worm

Sight word: **again**

Advanced words: **want, put, from, done**

One at a Time

"Look at me, Dad," cried Stan. "Can you see me?"

"No," said Dad. "I can't see you, Stan."

"Look up," said Stan. "Look up as high as you can. I'm on top of the world!"

"Oh, now I see," Dad said. "How did you get to the top of that tree?"

"I just came one branch at a time," Stan said.

"You did a good job," said Dad. "Now I want you to come down and help me. Do you see these seeds? I want you to plant them."

Stan came down, but not with a smile. He took the bag of seeds from Dad's hand.

Think and answer ■ ■ ■ ■ ■ ■ ■ ■ ■
Why do you think Stan said he was on top of the world?

"This is too much work," Stan said. "I can't plant all those seeds."

"Yes, you can," said Dad. "Tell me again—how did you get to the top of that tree?"

"One branch first, and then the next," said Stan.

"And that is how you can plant the seeds," Dad said. "One seed first, and then the next."

Stan did as Dad said. He put one seed in, and then the next. And then the next and the next and the next.

Soon no seeds were left in the bag.

He took the bag to Dad with a smile.

"You were right, Dad," he said. "One seed first and then the next. That's a good way to get work done. Now may I go back to the top of the world?"

"Yes," Dad smiled.

And soon Stan was high up in the tree again.

Think and answer ••••••••••
How could we use Dad's advice in our school work?

all
in ball

alk
in walk

| hall | tall | talk | rain/fall |
| call | small | chalk | side/walk |

1. I like to pray and talk with God.

2. A stalk of corn is a cornstalk.

3. Todd is small, but he can help his mother.

4. One day Todd will be a big, tall man.

Note: **a** before **ll** and **lk** says ô.

Words to Watch For

chalk	walk	talk
hall	ball	tall
birthday	baseball	surprise
	homework	

Sight word: **their**
Advanced words: **mother, they, done, put**

Birthday Twins

Kim and Tim are twins.

Kim is the girl twin, and Tim is the boy twin.

One day Mother said, "Twins, can you tell me what day it will be soon?"

"I can!" said Kim.

"I can!" said Tim.

"It will be our birthday," they both said.

"Then Kim will be six, and I will be six," said Tim. "We will both be six."

Think and answer ▪▪▪▪▪▪▪
Why do Kim and Tim have the same birthday?

"What do you want for
your birthday, Kim?" said
Mother.

"I want a doll," Kim said.
"I want a doll that can walk
and talk. Please may I have
a doll, Mother?"

"We will see," Mother
said. "And what do you
want, Tim?"

"I want a baseball," said Tim.

"A small, round baseball is what I want. And I want a bat to hit it with. May I have a bat and ball?"

"We will see," Mother said. "But now you both need to get your work done."

Kim and Tim went to work. Tim took out the trash for Mother. He did that job each day.

Kim made the beds and put the toys on the shelf. She kept her room clean and neat.

Then Kim and Tim got their books and sat down to read their homework.

"You both read well," said Mother. "You had to work hard to read that well. I just may have a surprise for you."

"What, Mother? What?" said Kim and Tim.

"Wait and see," said Mother. "Wait till your birthday, and you will see."

Think and answer ▪ ▪ ▪ ▪ ▪ ▪ ▪ ▪
What do you think the surprise might be?

This story continues on p. 63.

-ing

in pointing

looking   barking   walking   snowing

Read these words as fast as you can.

spell	burn	start
spells	burns	starts
spelling	burning	starting

Mark the correct word.

1. Mother is ____ my food.

   cook   cooks   cooking
   O   O   O

2. The owl ____ all night.

   hoot   hoots   hooting
   O   O   O

3. Tom's dog is ____ at the mailman.

   bark   barks   barking
   O   O   O

Note: A **suffix** is a letter or group of letters that comes at the end of a root word to make a new word. The **root word** is the original word, or the word that we begin with.

Read and Think

• •

Read these words as fast as you can.

storm	cheep	grow
storms	cheeps	grows
storming	cheeping	growing

• •

Mark the correct word.

Jim is ____.
  fish   fishes   fishing
   O   O   O

The fish will ____ the hook.
  bite   bites   biting
   O   O   O

Now Jim is ____ home.
   go   goes   going
   O   O   O

kn
in knot

gn
in gnat

know	knife	knack	gnash
knit	knight	knee	sign

Mark the correct word.

A ___ is a small fly.

knife   gnat
  o   o

I ___ what is right,
and I will do it.

know   knob
 o   o

Dad cut the meat
with his ___.

know   knife
 o   o

Note: **kn** and **gn** say **n.** (The **k** and **g** are silent.)

Words to Watch For

knee   gnat   know   open

Sight word: **Father**
Advanced words: **Mother, they**

The Big Day

Kim and Tim were in bed. Mother and Father were talking.

"The twins are a good help," said Mother. "They are reading well, too."

Think and answer ▪▪▪▪▪▪▪▪
How were the twins a good help?

"I'm proud of them," said Father. "Do you know what they want for their birth-day?"

"Yes," said Mother. "Kim wants a doll and Tim wants a bat and ball.

"I know we can get those for them. And I am think-ing of getting them a – – –."

"Shh," said Father. "Don't say it out loud. They might wake up."

"Then I am going to make it a surprise," said Mother. "It will be a surprise for you, too."

Mother kept her surprise well. She did not tell Kim and Tim, and she did not tell Father.

Soon the big day came.
It was the twins' birthday.
Kim and Tim had fun all
day.

Then it was time to eat.
Kim found a big box by her
plate. Tim found a big box
by his plate, too.

A small box was sitting next to Mother. The note on it said, "To Kim and Tim."

"I know what might be in my big box," said Kim. "But what is in the small one?"

"That's what I want to know," Tim said.

"Let's pray and eat," said Mother. "Then you may see."

The twins ate all their food. Then they had a birthday cake. Yum, it did taste good!

At last, Father said, "Now it's time to open the gifts."

Think and answer ■ ■ ■ ■ ■ ■ ■
What two things did the twins do before they
opened the gifts?

This story continues on p. 70.

ang
in bang

ing
in king

ong
in long

ung
in strung

hang	sing	dong	lung
clang	string	long	sung
sprang	thing	strong	swung

1. How do you like to go up in a swing?

2. "Ding, dong," sang the bell.

3. The bird has hurt its wing.

4. "Ouch, that bee stung me!" cried Matt.

 **ank**
in bank

ink
in wink

 **onk**
in honk

unk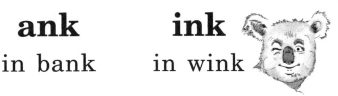
in trunk

Hank	link	blink	spunk
blank	wink	honk	plunk
yank	drink	dunk	junk

1. What is pink? A rose is pink.

2. Thank you, Lord, for the food
   we eat.

Mark the correct word.

I will keep these dimes in my ____.

   blink   honk   bank
    O   O   O

This cat is as black as ____.

  spank   ink   blink
   O   O   O

The Surprise Gift

Kim chose her big box first. "I think I know what this is," she said.

"I was right!" she cried. "It's a doll! It's a doll that can walk and talk."

Tim's big box had a bat and a ball in it. "I was right, too!" he said with a grin.

"Thank you, Mother and Father," the twins said again and again.

"Don't stop now," said Father. "I want to know what that small gift is. Mother did not tell me."

"I want to know, too," Kim said. "What is a gift that a boy and a girl will both like?"

Think and answer ■ ■ ■ ■ ■ ■ ■

Do you think the twins were thankful for their gifts?

How do you know?

Should we say, "Thank you," when we get a gift?

"We will know soon," said Father. "You take the string off, Kim."

Kim took the string off the box. Soon she held up a black book.

"It's a book," she said. "Look! It says B-I-B-L-E."

"It's a Bible!" Tim cried. "Now we can read our own Bible."

"Thank you, Mother," Kim and Tim said. "This is the best gift of all."

"I think so, too," said Father. "We can read it each night.

"Mother and I will help at first. But soon you will know how to read it, too."

Then Mother and Father and Kim and Tim sang a song. They sang, "The B-I-B-L-E, Yes, that's the book for me."

"Read it now, please," Tim said to Father.

And Father did.

Think and answer ━ ━ ━ ━ ■ ■ ■

Why is the Bible a good book to read every day?

Should we read it every day, too?

The B-I-B-L-E

The B-I-B-L-E,

Yes, that's the book for me;

I stand alone on the
Word of God:

The B-I-B-L-E.

Read and Think

Read these words as fast as you can.

small   talk   know   king   wink

squall   chalk   knife   sang   bank

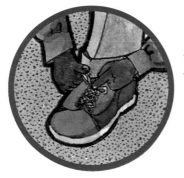

If I try again, I can get this knot out.

Mother will knit Ann a red cap.

Turn the door knob, Jim.

Read and Think

Write a word to rhyme with the words in each list.

1. stall
   fall
   call

2. thing
   cling
   sling

3. mink
   think
   pink

Songs of Praise

The Lord is good to all.
Praise ye the Lord.
Praise ye Him, sun and moon.
Praise Him, all ye stars of light.
Let them praise the
    name of the Lord.

O give thanks unto the Lord,
    for He is good.
Sing praise upon the harp
    unto our God.

All thy works shall praise thee,
    O Lord;
And thy saints shall bless Thee.

               — from the Psalms

Our Flag

Look at our flag. It stands for our land. What is the name of our land?

The flag has white stars on a blue back/ground. It has one star for each state. Do you know the name of our state?

Our flag has red and white stripes.

Can you count the stripes on the flag?

Our flag is red, white, and blue.

Red says, "Be brave."

White says, "Be pure."

Blue says, "Be true."

We will be brave, and pure, and true.

We love our flag. We love to see it wave.

Thank you, God, for our flag.

Think and answer ■ ■ ■ ■ ■ ■ ■

What is the name of our country?

What is the name of your state?

On the Farm

Steve and Jean live on a farm in the West. They like to play in the clean hay. Sometimes they wade in the brook.

Steve and Jean work hard to help out on the farm.

Think and answer ▪ ▪ ▪ ▪ ▪ ▪ ▪
What buildings do you think you might see on a farm?

Jean helps Mother cook and clean. She likes to help Father milk the cows.

Steve helps with the cows, too. He has a big farm dog, Shep. Steve and Shep take the cows to where the grass is green and long.

If a cow gets off the path, Steve has to bring it back. On some days he has to walk a long, long way.

At noon Jean goes out to get Steve. Then they both walk back to the house for lunch.

Steve gets a tall glass of cool milk. Milk tastes good to Steve, for he works hard with those cows.

Steve and Jean thank God for the meal. Jean thanks God for a tall, strong brother.

Steve thanks Him that he can work hard and be a help. They both thank God for a good home on the farm.

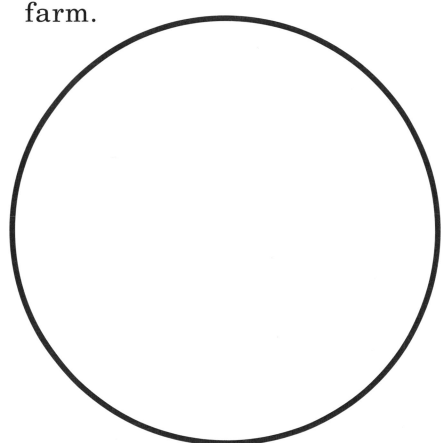

Make your own picture for the story here.

Think and answer ■ ■ ■ ■ ■ ■ ■ ■

What are some of the things Steve and Jean do to help out on the farm?

How do you help out at home?

Read and Think

Read these words as fast as you can.

spark	want	parch
Clark	wall	waste
chart	kink	carve
broom	wish	starve

Hank	farm
blank	charm
bring	walk
swing	stalk
high	good
nigh	wood

wa
in wash

want   wand   wasp   wan/der

1. I must wash my hands, and then I may eat.

2. My dog wags his tail to show that he likes me.

3. Don't waste this good food, Steve.

4. A wasp can sting like a bee.

a
in adopt

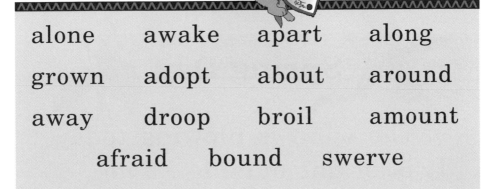

alone	awake	apart	along
grown	adopt	about	around
away	droop	broil	amount
	afraid	bound	swerve

1. I am not alone, for God is with me.

2. "Are you awake, Jim?" said Ted.

3. The two boys ran around the block.

4. Jean is not afraid of the dark.

When *a* comes at the beginning of a word, it usually says ŭ.

Words to Watch For

blowing   flying   singing   wander

Sight words: **Mr.   Mrs.**

Advanced words: **watch, pushing, done**

Spring Day

The wind is blowing today. It is bright outside. Two boys are flying kites on the hillside.

The birds are singing, and the plants are growing.

Mr. Burt is working in his yard. Mrs. Burt is working, too. Bill and Kay want to help. Bill will wa/ter the plants. Kay will watch Jon.

Jon is playing with his trucks.

He is pushing them around on the grass. He is small, and he can't work the way Bill and Kay can. Kay will not let Jon wander off.

Soon Bill and Kay will be done with their work. Then they will be playing, too.

Kay is thinking, "I like spring. All the world is awake and singing. What a glad day this is!"

Think and answer ∎ ∎ ∎ ∎ ∎ ∎ ∎
In this story, what are some signs that it is spring?

Read and Think

Say these words as fast as you can.

. . . .

alike	along	aside	awoke
shook	wasp	crown	clerk

. . . .

Draw lines to match:

harp

wasp

king

Read and Think

Draw lines to match:

fishing

knight

trunk

Mark the correct word.

1. Stan was fast ___.

    along   around   asleep
     O   O   O

2. I want to know all ___ the Bible.

    about   aside   awake
     O   O   O

3. Jesus ___ from the grave.

    alike   about   arose
     O   O   O

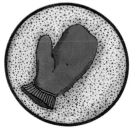

Syllables

Read the words. How many parts do you hear?

hope	pumping	surprise
afraid	stand	outside
splashing	baseball	abounding

Draw lines to match.

pillow

mitten

kitten

yellow

rabbit

hummingbird

Note: A **syllable** is a part of a word. Short words have only one syllable; long words have more than one syllable. Each syllable is sounded as a short word.

le
in little

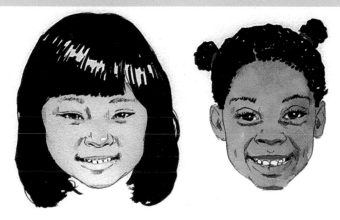

mid/dle	sad/dle	bot/tle	rab/bit
middle	saddle	bottle	rabbit

My kitten likes to snuggle up to me.

Do girls giggle more than boys do?

Mom fried pancakes on the griddle.

Mr. Higgins went up the ladder.

Note: A long word may be divided between double consonants. (Only one of the consonants is sounded.)

Note: When a long word ends with a consonant and *le,* the *e* is silent and l is usually the only sound heard in the last syllable.

y
in baby

pup/py	hap/py	pen/ny	dad/dy
puppy	happy	penny	daddy
happen	butter	rubber	slipper

Betty went shopping with her mom.

She got a pretty blue dress.

Jimmy likes to play ball with Tommy.

That baby is quite chubby.

Note: **y** at the end of a long word says ē.

Words to Watch For

Sight word: **once**
Advanced words: **brother, some, thought, from**

The Storm

Once a bad storm came to Ann's town. The north wind said, "Oo-oo-oo." The rain came down fast.

Ann was home alone with her little brother, Dave. Her father was at work, and her mother was downtown.

"I wish Mother and Father were here," thought Ann. "That wind makes me afraid. The puppy is afraid, too," thought Ann, as he began to howl.

"But if I cry, Dave will be afraid, too. I don't want to make him afraid. What can I do?"

Ann sat thinking. "If I do some work, that will help," she said. So she took down the broom and swept the floor.

Think and answer ■ ■ ■ ■ ■ ■ ■
Even though Ann was afraid, why didn't she cry?

But still she felt afraid.

"If I sing, that will help," she said. So she swept the floor and sang to little Dave.

But still she felt afraid.

"I know," she said at last. "I will think of a good Bible verse."

"I am thinking of a verse that will help us," she said to Dave.

"What time I am afraid,
I will trust in Thee."

Ann said that verse again and again.

"That helps," she said. "God made sunny days, and He made the wind and the rain. He made me, too, and little Dave. If we pray, God will help us to be brave."

Ann got down on her knees. Little Dave got down, too.

This is what Ann said:

"Lord, I will trust in You. I'm afraid now, but You can help me to be brave."

Ann got up. Little Dave got up, too.

Ann swept the floor and sang to Dave. And this time she did not feel afraid at all.

Soon Mother came home. "I know a good verse for storms," Ann said to Mother.

"What time I am afraid,

I will trust in Thee."

Think and answer ■ ■ ■ ■ ■ ■ ■
What helped Ann not to be afraid?

Will God's Word help *us* not to be afraid, too?

Words to Watch For

Skip/per   ap/ple   Tam/my

Advanced word: **something**

Summer Play

It was a hot summer day. Skipper and Sam were playing by the apple tree.

"What can we do on a hot day like this?" said Skipper.

"It's too hot to run, and I don't feel like reading. Can't you think of something fun to do?"

"I know!" said Sam. "I'll get the girls, and we can have a play."

"We can have it right here in the shade."

"Good!" said Skipper. "That sounds like fun."

Sam ran off to get the girls. Soon he came back with Kim, Tammy, and Pam.

"What will our play be about?" said Kim.

Think and answer ▪▪▪▪▪▪▪▪
What season of the year was it?
Were the children in school then?

Just then a noise came
from the apple tree.

"Tweet, tweet! Tweet,
tweet!"

"It can be about the birds," said Sam. "I'll be Mr. Bird and Tammy can be Mrs. Bird.

"The rest of you can be the little birds. Mrs. Bird and I will teach you something."

"Good!" they all said. "We like that."

So all five boys and girls went to work planning the play.

Soon you will see what it was all about.

Think and answer ■ ■ ■ ■ ■ ■ ■
What do you think Mr. and Mrs. Bird could teach baby birds?

Syllables

la/dy pre/tend ti/ger Bi/ble rob/in

lady pretend tiger Bible robin

chicken begin cable beside open

Read fast. **The Church**
Here's the church,
And here's the steeple.
Open the door
And see all the peo/ple!

Matching:

spider

cradle

baby

acorn

Note: A long word may be divided between a vowel and a consonant. (We do not separate *ck*.) The vowel at the end of a syllable is usually long.

Words to Watch For

Advanced words: **some, something, push**

Three
Baby Robins
A Play

Flippy: Tweet, tweet!

Flapppy: Tweet, tweet!

Floppy: Tweet, tweet!

Mrs. Robin: Here I come.

All the Baby Robins: Tweet, tweet! Tweet, tweet! Tweet, tweet!

Mrs. Robin: Open your mouths wide. I have something for you, and something for you, and something for you. Eat it up. Now say "Thank you."

All the Baby Robins: Tweet, tweet! Tweet, tweet! Tweet, tweet!

Mr. Robin: And now here I come. I have a fat worm for you, and one for you, and one for you. Eat them all up. Now say "Thank you."

Think and answer ▪ ▪ ▪ ▪ ▪ ▪ ▪ ▪
Are baby birds able to get their own food?

All the Baby Robins:
Tweet, tweet!
Tweet, tweet!

Mr. Robin: Now I'll fly and
get you some more.

Mrs. Robin: Here I come
again. This time I want
to teach you how to fly.

All the Baby Robins:
I'll try. I'll try. I'll try.

Mrs. Robin: That's my good
little birds. Come,
Flappy. You may try first.
Stand up in the nest.
Now look at me. I'm
going to fly from here
down to the ground.

Flappy: I see! I see! I see!

Mrs. Robin: Good! Now you fly down to me. Open your wings first. Now, jump up and fly. Good. Well done, Flappy.

Flappy: Tweet, tweet! I did it! I did it!

Mrs. Robin: Come, Flippy. You try next. Stand up in the nest and open your wings. Now, jump out and fly. That's the way! Well done, Flippy!

Flippy: Tweet, tweet! I did it! I did it!

Mrs. Robin: Come, Floppy. It's your turn. Stand up and try.

Floppy: No, no! No, no! No, no!

Mrs. Robin: Floppy!

Floppy: But I'm afraid.

Mr. Robin: Here I come with a fat worm. Where are you all?

Mrs. Robin: Look down here on the ground.

Flappy and Flippy: We can fly, Father! We can fly!

Think and answer ▪ ▪ ▪ ▪ ▪ ▪ ▪
Why do you think Floppy was afraid?

Mr. Robin: You good little birds! I'm proud of you. Open your mouths. Here is a good fat worm.

Floppy: Tweet, tweet! I want some!

Mr. Robin: Fly down here, and I will give you some, too.

Floppy: No, no! I'm afraid!

Mr. Robin: Then you can't have it. Come, Flappy! Come, Flippy! You shall have it all.

Floppy: Tweet, tweet! Tweet, tweet! Tweet, tweet!

Mrs. Robin: Don't cry so, Floppy! What do you want?

Floppy: I want a fat worm to eat.

Mr. Robin: Here it is for you, Floppy. Right here, see! Fly down and get it.

Floppy: I want to go, but I'm afraid.

Mrs. Robin: I'll come and help you start. Stand up, now, and open your wings. That's it. Now fly.

Mr. Robin: Fly to me. Come!

Floppy: I'm afraid! I'm afraid!

Mrs. Robin: I'll give you a push.

Floppy: Twee-ee-ee! I'm falling! No, I'm flying! Look at me fly! Look at me fly!

Mrs. Robin: Well done, Floppy!

Mr. Robin: Now you are all good birds, and down here you can get a lot to eat.

All the Baby Robins: Tweet, tweet! Tweet, tweet! Tweet, tweet!

Think and answer ....
Do you think Floppy is glad now that Mrs. Robin pushed him?
Are we sometimes afraid to try new things?

Syllables

gar/den   un/der   slum/ber   tim/ber
garden   under   slumber   timber

birthday   candy   dimple   winter

Read fast.   **Jack Be Nimble**
Jack be nimble,
Jack be quick,
Jack jump over
   the candlestick.

Matching:

turtle

wigwam

pilgrim

tadpole

Note: A long word may be divided between two consonants that are not alike.

Homes

A nest for the robin,
A hive for the bee,
A hole for the bunny,
And a fine house for me.

To Market, to Market

To market, to market,
to buy a fat pig,
Home again, home
again, jiggety-jig;
To market, to market,
to buy a fat hog,
Home again, home
again, jiggety-jog.

-ed
in wanted

"ĕd"

toasted	needed	pounded	mended
roasted	greeted	sounded	blended

Dad rented a big house.

Mom painted my bedroom blue.

I planted a row of beans.

Then we rested under the oak tree.

Note: The suffix *ed* says ĕd after a *t* or *d*.

-ed
in looked

talked   crashed   dressed   packed

walked   smashed   pressed   stacked

Mark the correct word.

1. Jane ____ the cake batter.
   wiped   kicked   mixed
   ○   ○   ○

2. Mom ____ hot dogs for lunch.
   cooked   brushed   huffed
   ○   ○   ○

3. Dad ____ me good night.
   dished   packed   kissed
   ○   ○   ○

4. We ____ in a trout stream.
   fished   crushed   thanked
   ○   ○   ○

Note: The suffix **ed** can say **t**.

-ed
"d"
in played

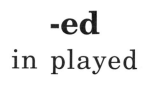

failed	prayed	grilled	broiled
mailed	strayed	spilled	spoiled

The baby spilled his milk.

Sport begged for his bone.

Mark the correct word.

1. It ___ all night, but now the sun is out.

   turned   rained   seemed

   ○   ○   ○

2. We ___ across the lake in a rowboat.

   oiled   cleaned   rowed

   ○   ○   ○

Note: The suffix *ed* can say **d.**

Read and Think

Fun with *-ed*

Dad washed the car.
Jan helped Mom cook.
Jack chased a frog
Into the brook.

Dad roasted hot dogs.
Mom baked a cake.
How many *-ed* words
Can you make?

• •

Draw lines to match.

1. Bill ___ the horn at the dog.   painted

2. The boat ___ across the bay.   sailed

3. Dad ___ the house blue.   honked

4. We ___ to the creek to fish.   walked

• •

One, Two,
Buckle My Shoe

One, two,
Buckle my shoe;

Three, four,
Knock at the door;

Five, six,
Pick up sticks;

Seven, eight,
Lay them straight;

Nine, ten,
A good fat hen.

Little Boy Blue

Little Boy Blue,
   come blow your horn,
The sheep's in the meadow,
   the cow's in the corn;
But where is the little boy
   that looks after the sheep?
He's under the haystack,
   fast asleep.
Will you wake him? No, not I;
For if I do, I'm afraid he'll cry.

Rain

The rain is raining all around,
It falls on field and tree,
It rains on the umbrellas here,
and on the ships at sea.

Thank You

Thank You for the world so sweet,
Thank You for the food we eat,
Thank You for the birds that sing,
Thank You, God, for everything.

Special Sounds
introduced in *Stepping Stones*

Chart 8

thr in **thr**ee	**ir** in b**ir**d
ar in st**ar**s	**oi** in c**oi**n
ch in **ch**ur**ch**	**oy** in b**oy**
or in m**or**ning	**oo** in b**oo**k
ou in **ou**t	**oo** in t**oo**th
ow in **ow**l	**wor** in **wor**ms
ow in b**ow**l	**igh** in n**igh**t
er in v**er**se	**all** in b**all**
ur in n**ur**se	**alk** in w**alk**

Chart 9

-ing in point**ing**	**onk** in h**onk**
kn in **kn**ot	**unk** in tr**unk**
gn in **gn**at	**wa** in **wa**sh
ang in b**ang**	**a** in **a**dopt
ing in k**ing**	**y** in bab**y**
ong in l**ong**	**le** in litt**le**
ung in str**ung**	**-ed** in want**ed**
ank in b**ank**	**-ed** in look**ed**
ink in w**ink**	**-ed** in play**ed**

Secrets and Surprises is the next book in the first grade reading program. It reviews Charts 8 and 9 and introduces words with special sounds from Charts 10 and 11.